CONTENTS

D0317543

CHAPTER ONE:
THE FIRST VOYAGE

. . . As a young man, I inherited considerable wealth from my father.

After wasting much of it, I invested the rest in a sturdy ship and a brave crew. We set sail to seek out the secret wonders of the world.

Adventure found us quickly.

An island?! That can't be! None of our charts show an island in these waters.

Stop complaining, Ali. Maybe we'll finally find some fresh water and food.

With a firm hold on the giant beast, I travelled into unknown seas.

Finally, I spotted an island, released my grip, and washed up on another shore.

I entered the jungle in search of fresh water and food . . .

What I found on the other side was amazing.

17

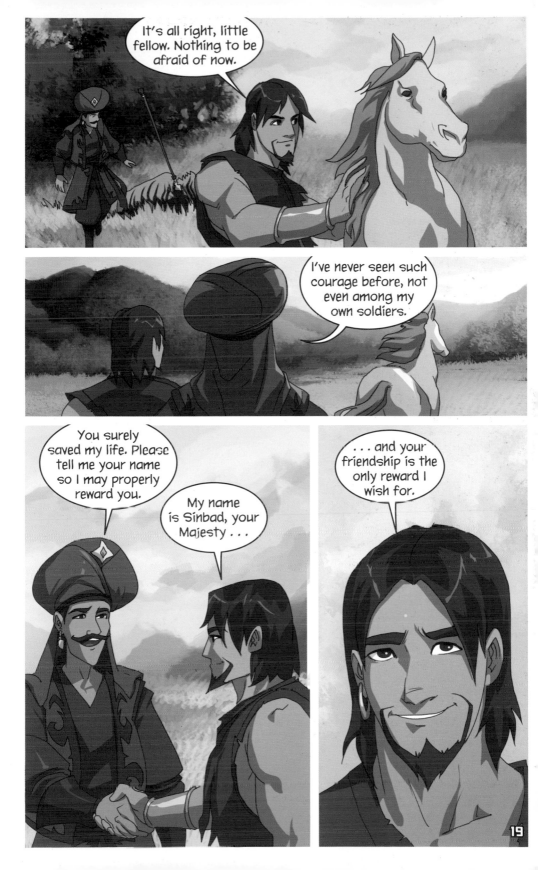

It was a monstrous bird known as the Roc!

They had been known to carry away fully-grown elephants.

SKEEEEEVVV!!

CHAPTER THREE:
THE THIRD VOYAGE

We lost count of the days and the nights as we were carried across the sea.

Finally, we spotted an island and dived towards our freedom.

By chance, we had discovered the legendary Thunder Island!

No one had ever journeyed there and lived to tell of it.

It was a frightful place . . .

Keep watching the pretty colours.

Jabbu, Ali . . . hand me one of those sharpened roasting spits.

The Cyclops had become hypnotized by the gleaming diamond . . .

It would be the last thing the monster would ever see.

NOW!

GRR-ROWWWRRR!!

CHAPTER FOUR:
THE FOURTH VOYAGE

My good fortune didn't last. Soon after, a terrible tempest cast me overboard . . .

I don't know how long I was adrift for.

Sick from thirst and fever, I was barely aware of being rescued and taken to a fog-shrouded island.

We glided through the heavy mist . . .

. . . and I dimly wondered if I was still alive.

37

39

Weeks passed, and my captors continued to supply me with food. The terrible truth dawned on me . . . Harran and the others had been fattened up.

I was a prisoner of cannibals.

From then on, I lived off only a little coconut milk, purposely growing thinner each day . . .

Finally, I was able to slip through the prison bars.

The wind sped along my canoe. In a few days, I discovered an island with lush trees and colourful fruit.

Paradise.

Or so I'd thought . . .

Halt! I am Prince Kelan. Explain your presence on my island.

Sinbad, the legendary sea sailor? You are welcome, indeed! Come, we are anxious to hear of your adventures!

My name is Sinbad, your Majesty.

I'm a castaway, very far from home.

Good as his word, Prince Kelan warmly received me into his grand palace.

I entertained the court with tales of my perilous travels.

Poor Sari was very ill. I could do nothing but try to comfort her.

The end came quickly while she slept . . .

I mourned beside her brother at the funeral ceremony.

Suddenly, as the funeral ended . . .

Prince Kelan –!

What's happening? Why are you doing this?!

According to our laws a man must be buried with his wife, even if he still lives.

Farewell, Sinbad.

Forgive me.

Buried alive!!

I struggled with the ropes until I collapsed from exhaustion.

Once awakened, I was surprised that I'd been freed . . .

Fresh sea air led me to a sloping tunnel somewhere deep beyond the tomb.

Someone was guiding me at the far end of the tunnel, flashing a shiny signal.

The tide was rising, and the sea water grew deeper with every step. I was fearful of drowning, but this was my only escape.

47

Only when I'd surfaced did I see my mermaid saviour. Once again, the sea had saved me . . .

Soon, I reunited with my crew, and we set sail on another adventure.

CHAPTER FIVE:
THE FIFTH VOYAGE

A great dome! Perhaps it's the palace of a powerful magician!

It's perfectly smooth – without windows or doors.

I can't hear anything. Maybe no one's home.

Back away! This could only be one thing . . .

CHAPTER SIX: THE SIXTH VOYAGE

The Roc's beating wings had separated us, and soon my crew had vanished into the darkness and distance.

I could only hope that, somewhere, they had found a friendly shore.

My new land was as strange as any I'd seen, a place where rivers ran rich with precious gems.

I was welcomed kindly, as stories had spread of my voyages.

Even in the furthest corners of the world, everyone knew the name of Sinbad.

The king himself offered me endless riches to remain in his beautiful land, but there was only one thing I truly wanted . . .

Of course, I will grant your request, Captain Sinbad.

Our very finest ship shall be yours.

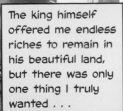

Armed with a bow and poison arrows, I crept through the jungle in search of the elephants.

It didn't take me long to find the gentle, grazing giants.

I thought of Serena and took careful aim.

I cannot do it. There is no honour in killing innocent beasts.

There must be another way to save Serena.

58

Serena –! Where are we going? I don't understand . . .
You will, just follow me. Be careful, these dungeon stairs are slippery.
There's the key, still hooked to the wall!
You're not the only one full of surprises, Sinbad. What do you say now?
My dreams have come true . . . !

Instead, the young cobbler bought himself a sturdy ship and a courageous crew.

Captain Hindba's own great adventure was just beginning!

ARABIAN NIGHTS

The story of Sinbad the Sailor is part of a collection of Middle Eastern and South Asian folktales known as *One Thousand and One Nights*. These tales have been passed down from generation to generation for hundreds of years. The first English-language edition, entitled *Arabian Nights' Entertainments*, was published in 1706.

Since then, many versions of the book have been published – some containing more than 1,000 stories. In each of these editions, the tales of mystery and adventure are told by the same narrator, a beautiful woman named Scheherazade. She has just married an evil ruler who plans to kill her before the night is through. To stop him, Scheherazade entertains the king with a new story each night, and he soon forgets about his deadly plan.

The Arabian Nights tales remains some of the greatest stories ever told. They include popular adventures, such as "The Fisherman and the Genie", "The Seven Voyages of Sinbad", and "Ali Baba and the Forty Thieves". Many of these stories have been adapted into films, books, and plays that are still popular today.

REAL-WORLD EXPLORERS

FERDINAND MAGELLAN

On 10 August 1519, this Spanish sailor left Seville, Spain, with five ships and a large crew. He returned three years later, becoming the first explorer to sail around the world. During his voyage, Magellan navigated through the southern strait of South America, which connects the Alantic and Pacific Oceans. It is now called the Strait of Magellan.

JUAN PONCE DE LEÓN

In the early 1500s, many believe this explorer set out from Spain in search of the Fountain of Youth. Although he didn't succeed, Ponce de León became the first European to visit what would become known as America, setting foot in Florida in 1513.

ROBERT EDWIN PEARY

On 6 July 1908, this Pennsylvania man left New York City with one goal - to reach the North Pole. Nearly one year later, he became the first man to accomplish this gruelling feat.

ABOUT THE AUTHOR

Since 1986, Martin Powell has been a freelance writer. He has written hundreds of stories, many of which have been published by Disney, Marvel, Tekno Comix, Moonstone Books, and others. In 1989, Powell received an Eisner Award nomination for his graphic novel *Scarlet in Gaslight*. This award is one of the highest comic book honours.

ABOUT THE ILLUSTRATOR

Ferran was born in Monterrey, Mexico, in 1977. For more than a decade, Ferran has worked as a colourist and an illustrator for comic book publishers such as Marvel, Image, and Dark Horse. He currently works for Protobunker Studio while also developing his first graphic novel.

GLOSSARY

ancient very old

beggar someone who asks for money or help on the street

cannibal someone who eats human flesh

cursed under an evil spell

cyclops monster with a single eye in the middle of its forehead

desolate deserted or uninhabited

fiend evil or cruel person

hypnotize place someone into a trance

legend story handed down from earlier times, which is often based on facts but not entirely true

lurking moving stealthily to avoid being seen

marooned stuck on a deserted island and unable to leave

merchant someone who sells goods for profit

monsoon very strong wind that blows across the Indian Ocean and southern Asia

tempest violent storm or uproar

DISCUSSION QUESTIONS

1. At the end of the story, why do you think Sinbad gave the beggar a large diamond? How did Sinbad hope he would spend it? Explain.

2. Sinbad the Sailor had seven exciting adventures at sea. Which voyage do you think was the most exciting? Explain your answer.

3. Each page of a graphic novel is made up of several illustrations called panels. Which panel of art was your favourite? Why?

WRITING PROMPTS

1. Keep a diary of your own explorations. Write about the places you've been and the adventures you've had.

2. Sinbad had seven voyages. Pretend you're the author and imagine an eighth adventure. Where will the explorer go next? What types of creatures will he face? You decide.

3. Imagine your own Arabian Nights tale. Think of a story filled with mystery and adventure. Then write it down and read it to friends and family.

ARABIAN NIGHTS TALES

ALADDIN AND THE MAGIC LAMP

The legendary tale of Aladdin, a poor youth living in the city of Al Kal'as. One day, the crafty boy outsmarts an evil sorcerer, getting his hands on a magical lamp that houses a wish-fulfilling genie! Soon, all of Aladdin's dreams come true, and he finds himself married to a beautiful princess. All is well until, one day, the evil sorcerer returns to reclaim the lamp.

ALI BABA AND THE FORTY THIEVES

The legendary tale of Ali Baba, a young Persian boy who discovers a cave filled with gold and jewels, the hidden treasures of 40 deadly thieves. Unfortunately, his greedy brother, Kassim, cannot wait to get his hands on the riches. Returning to the cave, he is captured by the thieves and killed, and now the evil men want revenge on Ali Baba as well.

THE SEVEN VOYAGES OF SINBAD

The tale of Sinbad the Sailor, who goes to sea in search of great riches and discovers even greater adventures. On his seven treacherous voyages, the Persian explorer braves a shipwreck, fights off savage cannibals, and battles a giant Cyclops, hoping to survive and tell his legendary story.

THE FISHERMAN AND THE GENIE

The legendary tale of an evil Persian king, who marries a new wife each day and then kills her the next morning. To stop this murderous ruler, a brave woman named Scheherazade risks her own life and marries the king herself . . . but not without a plan. On their wedding night, she will entertain him with the tale of the Fisherman and the Genie – a story so amazing, he'll never want it to end.